A Bug
and a
Pup

by Lynn Trepicchio
illustrated by
James Williamson

Harcourt

Orlando   Boston   Dallas   Chicago   San Diego

Visit *The Learning Site!*

www.harcourtschool.com

Here is a bug.
Can he come out?

The bug is little.
He can come out.

Here is a pup.
Can he come out?

4

The pup is big.
He can come out.

The bug sees
the pup.

6

"Look out pup!
I'll get you!"

What a surprise!